Between the edge of the Sahara Desert and the foot of the Atlas Mountains of Morocco lies the village of Tafsa. It is a small village which has changed little since biblical times; in fact, it seems almost as if it has been forgotten by civilization. Here lives Mohammed ben Ibrahim, the Berber boy, who through the pages of this book shares with the reader some of the experiences of his daily life.

It is Monday and Mohammed loads his donkey for a visit to a nearby village where he will sell the pottery his father has made in the course of the past week. The *souk* — the Berber market — is a place bustling with activity, where the variety of the merchandise is matched by its many aromas. It is a place where the *caïd* — the local official — sits in judgment and the storyteller entertains the crowd while the merchants call attention to their wares with shrill cries.

Independence Day follows the *souk* day, and it is cause for a great celebration. The Berber dancers in their colorful costumes compete with each other until the day is climaxed by the *fantasia*, a wild, joyful charge of horses and riders.

The reader will also meet Mohammed's hard-working family, visit his home, be present at their frugal meals, and learn many other aspects of their lives as well as some of the colorful legends and stories that are part of Mohammed's tradition and that of his country.

MOUNTAINS

Road to Marrakesh→

Mosque

Omar is plowing here

Olive trees

Barbers

Date sellers

Medicine stalls

Ahlish village

Grain souk

Pottery souk

Oil sellers

Bakers

Ropemaker

Cloth souk

Meat souk

Grocery sellers

A. M. JAUSS

My Village in Morocco

SONIA AND TIM GIDAL

PANTHEON BOOKS

The authors acknowledge with grateful
appreciation the assistance given to them
by the Moroccan Office of Tourism in Rabat.

All rights reserved under International and Pan-
American Copyright Conventions. Published in New
York by Pantheon Books, a division of Random House,
Inc., and simultaneously in Toronto, Canada, by Ran-
dom House of Canada, Limited. Manufactured in the
United States of America.

Library of Congress catalog card number: 64-18316

My Village in Morocco

I

My name is Mohammed ben Ibrahim, Mohammed the son of Ibrahim.

There are many boys by the name of Mohammed around here, because this was the name of the great Prophet, who founded our Islamic religion.

I live in North Africa in the Kingdom of Morocco. We call it also El Maghreb el Aksa, which means "The Farthest West," because of all Islamic countries, none is farther west than ours. Our village, Tafsa, lies in the valley of the Ourika River, at the foot of the great Atlas Mountains.

I am a Moslem, and a Berber of the Aït-Slimane clan. My family belongs to the Rhirhaia tribe. Abba, my father, told me that the Berbers came here more than five thousand years ago and were the first settlers in North Africa. He doesn't know why the Berbers migrated here, but he says we are Hamites, descendants of Ham, one of the three sons of Noah, who built the Ark. The Arabs came to El Maghreb much later than the Berbers. The Arabs are Semites, descendants of the *oldest* son of Noah, whose name was Sem.

Abba says nobody knows who first called us "Berbers," which means "foreigners." It is not our real name. We call ourselves Imazighen, which means "Free Men," and that is what we really are, says Abba, because our people were never conquered.

2

Abba is a potter. Nearly all the men in our village are potters. They make water jars and cooking pots and bowls from the red clay we dig out of the banks of the Ourika River, down in the valley below.

Tafsa stretches all the way up the hill. The shrine of our saint, Tabouri, is on the square halfway up, where the women meet at the well when they do their laundry. Sometimes the storyteller comes there, and then almost everybody squats on the ground in a circle around him and listens to his tales and songs.

The big house on top of the hill belongs to our Sheik. He and the *taleb*, the teacher in our Koran school, are the only people in the village whose window holes are decorated with wrought-iron grilles.

3

We other villagers have only small openings in the walls, which are closed at night with wooden shutters from the inside. To make the openings look pretty, we often paint a white or blue frame around them.

Our house lies on a steep bank above the road, which leads high up over the Atlas Mountains and far, far away to the deserts in the south. In the other direction, the road leads to the city of Marrakesh and on and on till one comes to Casablanca, where there are thousands of big white houses, and to Rabat, where our King reigns in his great palace. But I have never seen a city in all my life.

There are always people on the road, caravans and peddlers and potters with their wares, and people going to or coming from the market, even at night.

Our house consists of four rooms. The bricks are made of pressed mud mixed with straw. They were dried in the sun until they became quite hard. The finished walls were plastered with another layer of mud and the sun dried it again. The two rooms in the front are covered by a single roof, also of dried mud, spread over reeds and brushwood. Abba built our house himself.

The room to the right is my father's workshop. To the left is the shed for our cow, our mule, and our donkey and the six sheep and four goats. The kitchen and our sleeping room are on the other side of the little courtyard.

When the sun rises over the valley of Ourika, our *taleb* hoists a white flag on the roof of the Koran school. He is our *muezzin* too, our caller to prayer. "Prayer is better than sleep!" he shouts through his cupped hands to the four sides of the wind. "God is most great! I testify that there is no God but Allah and Mohammed is His Prophet!" Then our day begins.

My older sister, Latifa, helps me carry the *gidrahs*, the big water jars, down to the road. Later we will load them on our donkey and take them to the weekly *souk*, the market of the Ourika Valley. Latifa carries my brother Hamidu on her back. He was six moons old last *souk* day. I know, because he got his first haircut then, as every boy does at this age. This is our custom. Only one single lock of hair was

4

left, for the angels of Allah to pull him up to heaven by if he dies as a child.

"Look, Latifa, there are fingerprints on this jar," I say. "I can't take it to the *souk!*"

"It must have been Ahmed again!" Latifa complains. "I chased him away from the wet pottery yesterday, when he kept teasing me. I will slap him this time for spoiling the jar with his fingerprints!" And she rushes off angrily. Soon she is back, pulling Ahmed along over the ground by one leg.

"I didn't spoil the jar!" he wails, when Latifa presses his nose against it. "I only made a hand of Fatima to bring us good luck! Don't you want good luck?"

Fatima was the daughter of our Prophet Mohammed. The women and girls wear bracelets and necklaces of silver in the form of Fatima's hand for good luck. But Ahmed's answer is just an excuse for his mischief.

"Spoiling a precious jar and calling it good luck!" I scold him. "If you play such a stupid joke again, I'll dunk your face in the mud. Press your hand on your own things, or I'll make a mudhead of you!" Latifa lets him off with a good slap on his behind.

My upper lip is itching. That means I will soon meet an old friend. Who would that be, I wonder. And when? And where? I squat down to think about it quietly.

"Mohammed! Mohammed! *Ashi hena!*" Jima, my mother, calls from the house. "Come here!"

I run up to her. Many clay jars lie right and left, in the sun to dry. The best place for them is on the big stones which the villagers brought up and dumped on each side of the little tracks leading to the houses. The sun-heated stones give off warmth and help dry the jars from the underside too.

"Feed the donkey some grass and dates and start packing the jars," Jima tells me. "Ask Abba for the rope net, and take as many dates along as you have jars. Eat one every time you sell a jar and keep the pits; this way you can keep track of how many you sell."

6

"*Na'am!*" I answer. "Yes! And what shall I bring back from the market? Plenty of henna, certainly!"

"Plenty I cannot afford, silly," Jima laughs. "But seventeen grams will do for tomorrow's festival and for the next few weeks. Buy it from Kadur ben Mohammed. He sells it cheapest."

Henna is an orange-red powder made from the leaves of a wild plant. The girls and women make a paste of henna and water and paint their fingernails and the palms of their hands with it, to be beautiful. But it is also healthy, they say, and the *jinn*, the evil spirits, don't like the scent of the henna and keep away. They don't like salt either, so when I am afraid of the *jinn* at night, I put a pinch of it under my sleeping mat. Latifa says it's even better to eat some salt if one wants to keep the evil spirits away. Once, when she got frightened, she swallowed a whole handful. She almost choked, and that terrified her even more. The *jinn* must have had fun when they saw it.

Jima always smears some henna on our cow and on the goats and sheep too, and even on the chickens, so the evil *jinn* won't have power to harm them either.

"Are you dreaming, Mohammed?" I hear my mother say. "What did I tell you to bring me?"

"Henna," I answer, "seventeen grams."

"And . . ."

". . . and . . . and . . . salt?"

"Take a piece of paper and write it down, or I will get everything except what I need! Write, *one:* a skullcap for Grandfather Yussuf. His old *tagia* is torn, and he can't wear it if he goes to the festival tomorrow. Brown or blue, and no design on it. *Two:* one piece of soap. Take the cheapest. *Three:* four or five bundles of mint leaves for the tea. Look for juicy green ones, fresh and strong-smelling. *Four:* one kilo of dates. Take only dry ones, not sticky, not pressed. They will be easier to take along tomorrow, and won't smear. Have you got it all?"

"*Na'am,*" I answer, "yes — not sticky, not pressed. Is that all?"

"Not yet! *Five:* if you have enough money after you have sold the *gidrahs,* buy a cone of sugar. Have you written down everything?"

"Yes, I have," I say. "Shall I show you?"

"I'll show *you* something, you impudent monkey!" Jima answers, and before I can duck she has tweaked my nose.

Jima can't read or write and doesn't like to be teased about it. Hardly anybody in our village can write or read, but I was sent for three rainy seasons and two dry seasons to the Koran school, where I learned both.

"And now go to your father and ask what else you are to bring from the *souk!*"

Abba is standing in his workshop, preparing the clay for a new *gidrah.* In the morning he crushed the dry clay to powder. Now he sifts ten handfuls of it through a sieve and mixes it with one handful of fine powder from old potsherds to temper the mixture. He adds water and kneads the mixture on a flat stone, till it has the right consistency. Abba makes about twenty *gidrahs* and bowls each day on his potter's wheel, and he works seven days a week from sunrise to sundown.

"Wait till I have kneaded the clay," Abba says, "then we can start loading the donkey. And Mohammed, sell the *gidrahs* first, before you wander around the *souk.* Don't forget to pick up the new net I ordered from Hassan the ropemaker."

"I want to go with Mohammed," my small sister Hadidsha wails. "I can help him sell the *gidrahs.*"

"I am happy if you don't *break* one!" Abba laughs. "But give me that empty sardine can you are holding. I will fill it with clay for you, and you can make your own bowl — *that* you may sell in the village if you can find a customer!"

"No, I can't. Everybody makes his own bowls here. You are just teasing me.

But Jiddy will paint it for me beautifully, I am sure of that!"

"I am, too," says my sister Latifa, "because you know how to pester him long enough." Meanwhile little Hamidu on her back has fallen asleep.

Latifa is always serious, and Hadidsha is always laughing and teasing, but she *does* get Jiddy, our grandfather, to do things for her more easily than anyone else. She and Ahmed are the clever ones in our family.

I feed our donkey some grass. Jima gives me a piece of *chubz,* our flat bread, some olives, and twenty dates, one for each *gidrah* I am taking to the *souk.* I put them in my *shkara,* the camel-leather bag I always carry around my shoulders. The slip of paper I put in the hood of my *djellaba,* the long hooded cloak of wool I am wearing. Then I ride the donkey down to the road.

Many vessels lie drying in the sun between the stones and the cactus bushes. Not a single flower and no grass grows around our village; it is all arid soil here. Only on the banks of the Ourika River, down in the valley, do we have a small strip of grazing land for the animals, and this land belongs to the whole village.

Abba and Jima have laid out the *gidrah* net on the ground. On it we stack the twenty *gidrahs* carefully in three layers. Abba then ties

11

up the net on top. All together we now heave the bundle onto the back of the donkey. He stands quietly with his heavy load and doesn't even bray.

"May Allah give you a hand at the *souk!*" Jiddy Yussuf calls to me from the roadside where he sits decorating bowls. "Sell well, O son of

my son. The first *gidrah* you sell, give away as a bargain! This will draw other customers to you. People like to hear of bargains. And Mohammed, before you start selling, take a good look around. If there is much pottery on the market, sell cheap, or you won't sell at all. If there is little, you can ask higher prices."

With that, he dips his little brush into a cup of green color and slowly draws a design on the clay bowl in his hand. Jiddy prepares all his colors himself from the roots of wild plants and the skins of onions.

"Mohammed," he continues, "I haven't gone to the Ahlish market for a long time. Go to the medicine stalls and ask for my old friend Kadur. Tell him that my backache is worse than ever. He will give you some of his herbs or ointments. The last time, he sent me some *sahtar* herb, to rub on my back, but it didn't help very much. May you never have such a backache, O Mohammed!" But while he complains, he smiles as if the backache was fun to have.

"I will bring you a medicine for your backache, Jiddy," I promise. "May your pains disappear very fast. May the stork take them all away!" And I point to the stork that is just settling on the roof of our house.

"*Insh'allah! Insh'allah!*" Jiddy calls. "May it be Allah's will! My heart is gladdened and my pains are lessened already now that I see the stork! He has chosen our house for his nest. Surely there is no better sign of a happy time than this, Allah be praised." He smiles and his leathery face shows even more wrinkles than usual. "Allah be with you, Mohammed!"

"Allah be with you a hundred times, Jiddy." I press my stick to the donkey's side and we start on the way to the Monday *souk* at Ahlish village.

II

Wandering along to the market is fun. There are always people on our roads, and everybody has time for a talk. In front of me, I see my friend Mohammed driving his donkey to the market too. We stop to greet each other, and walk on side by side. We talk of Marrakesh, which we hope to visit one day. There, storytellers and snake charmers and musicians and dancers entertain all day long on the big market square, which is called Djemaa el Fna, the "Meeting Place of the Dead." It got this name because it is said that in former times criminals had their heads cut off there, and put on long poles.

It takes only three days to walk to Marrakesh. "All we need for the journey is a few *dirhams* to buy sardines and a loaf of bread a day," says Mohammed. "Our parents would give us dates and sugar and mint tea."

"We could collect brushwood for the fire on the way," I suggest, "and we could sleep on the ground, wrapped up in our *djellabas*." The *djellabas* would keep us warm, even if the nights should get very cold.

"I think we'll have to wait," says Mohammed, "till somebody needs a shepherd or two to drive sheep or goats to Marrakesh. It sometimes happens. That way we could make a few *dirhams*."

Just then a big herd of sheep and goats crosses the road. We are in their way, and so they press against us and our donkeys. I'm afraid that with the heavy load on his back my donkey will kick and lose his balance. If he falls, some of the *gidrahs* will break. We both start kicking and cursing the sheep and goats like anything. "*Yallah! Yallah!*" we shout. "Go! Go! May the *jinn* chase you!"

The shepherd comes running. "Watch your tongue, Mohammed ben Ibrahim!" he shouts. With a whistle, he guides his flock across the road, and then he turns to us again.

"Don't you know better than to curse?" he says. "Never call on an evil spirit for help, Mohammed! It may turn against yourself!"

14

"*Saba el cheh*," I say courteously. "Good morning! May my words be made unspoken. I was only afraid my *gidrahs* would break and I didn't know what I was saying. But how, for the love of Allah, do you know my name?"

The shepherd laughs. "Your eyes were elsewhere, when I talked to your father in the *souk*, but I saw *you*. You were watching a snake charmer then. I am Mohammed ben Rahman, of Ahlish village."

"My father's *taleb!*" I exclaim. "May Allah gladden your face. Are you not a *taleb* any more?"

"Not for years now. A good *taleb* takes up teaching the *surahs* of the Glorious Koran when he feels he is needed, but he shouldn't make it his profession forever. My soul is as happy guarding sheep and goats as it was teaching boys. Greet your father from me; he was a good pupil — I never heard *him* curse! His son should never curse either! *Ma'al salama*, Mohammed! — Peace be with you!"

"*Wa' selam!*" we call back, and I add: "May Allah increase your sheep and goats!"

"*Zahemak!*" I say to my friend when we are out of earshot. "Fool! Couldn't you have found a few words to help me out when we were caught by my father's old *taleb*, of all people? We were both swearing, weren't we? You stood there all the time like a clay pot with an open mouth painted on it!"

"I even *felt* like a clay pot, I can tell you. I am happy he didn't recognize *me!* May Allah save me from my mother's anger if he should tell her! She is quick with a sandal on my head, you know that." And he lets out a howl as if he had just been hit.

A little boy eyes us suspiciously while he passes us on his donkey, which is loaded with green fodder.

"*Salama*, little one!" I call to him. "Peace be with you and your donkey! My friend here was only joking, don't be afraid. Are you riding to the *souk* too?"

"I don't know," he answers. "I am Hamid ben Mustafa and I am thirsty."

"I am sorry," I say, "but our waterbags are empty. Are you going to sell the fodder?"

"I don't know," Hamid answers again. "I am thirsty."

16

"We are almost at the well," I console him. "You can drink as much as you like there. Are you *very* thirsty?"

"I don't know," he answers, "but I am thirsty."

"Mohammed," I say to my friend, "run ahead and see whether there is a leather bucket at the well; if not, one of us had better walk to the hut over there and ask for one. I will take care of your donkey meanwhile. And you, thirsty one, don't be afraid: I'm going to give your donkey a push. He will get you to the well faster then."

I slap the donkey, and he falls into a nice trot. Little Hamid jumps up and down on his load, but he isn't afraid at all. *"Yallah ruah!"* he shouts. "Go quick! *Yallah ruah!"*

When we reach the well, Mohammed has just drawn up a bucketful of water. The little boy drinks from his cupped hands, and then we heave him onto his donkey again.

"Are you happy now?" Mohammed asks him.

"I don't know," he answers, " . . . I am thirsty!" We laugh out loud at that, and Mohammed says, "Now I understand our Berber saying: 'Silly people are thirsty even when they are in the water.' Allah be with you, silly one!"

"I am not silly," he answers. "I am not silly! I am thirsty!" And he trots on.

"Let's drink ourselves now," I suggest, as we fill up our waterbags. Before we continue on our way to the *souk*, we water our donkeys. The sun is very hot now, and we pull our hoods over our heads. The heavier I am dressed, the better my body is protected from the heat, and the less quickly do I get thirsty.

"My uncle Omar!" shouts Mohammed. "Over there, plowing with his mule and camel." We stop our donkeys and walk over.

"*Saba el cheh!*" we greet him. "May your plowing bring you a good harvest!"

"Allah sends His blessings as He wishes," Omar answers, "but one still has to sow enough seed if one wants to reap enough grain. And I just haven't got enough seed this year after last year's crop failure. I had to sell all my sheep to buy seed for this field, and I haven't enough fodder left even for my donkey. Look how his ribs stand out!"

"May Allah gladden your face," I say, "and give you a better harvest next time."

"*Insh'allah!*" he answers. "I am going to get a loan from the money-lender till the next harvest to buy food for my six children. There is

18

no oil or sugar in my house any more — and look at all the cursed cowbirds up there in the tree! I have to chase them away all the time to keep them from eating the seed I am sowing."

"But the cowbirds pick the ticks from the fur of your camel, too. So they are good for something, at least," I say, to calm his anger.

"I know! What's bad for me is good for the camel — what can I do? Anyway, these are all *my* troubles. May Allah send you good customers at the *souk*, boys! *Ma'al salama!*"

We say goodbye and walk on. The road is getting crowded now with people and donkeys on their way to the *souk*. They are loaded with pottery and eggs and vegetables, with chickens and horseshoes and cereal seed and sugar cones and bags of rice and many other foodstuffs. My friend Mohammed has fallen behind, and I wait for him. When he catches up at last, a whole caravan of potter's donkeys are behind him. I am afraid I will have to sell cheap today, if I want to get rid of my twenty *gidrahs*.

"Where have you been so long?" I ask Mohammed.

"I stepped on some big thorns," he answers. "My left foot hurts. I couldn't walk faster."

"The blacksmith passed me a few moments ago," I tell him. "He knows how to take out thorns from donkey's feet! You should go to him; he will help you!"

"It's you who have donkey's feet, you *gidrah*-head!" he says, scowling. But I know he will go to the horseshoe man anyway, who really is good at taking out splinters and thorns.

When we come to the signpost which says: 2 KILOMETERS MONDAY SOUK OF OURIKA, we turn off the main road. All our signposts are written in both Arabic and French, because for many years most of Morocco was governed by France. But we became independent in 1956. Even now, most people in the government schools learn French, but I speak only the Berber language. I understand Arabic also, though not too well, and French I do not understand at all. But I

know it is written from left to right instead of the proper way from right to left, like Berber and Arabic.

At last we come to the Ourika River. In early spring, when the snow is melting on the High Atlas Mountains, the water in the *wadi*, the river bed, rises so high that the bridge cannot even be seen. Then the currents are too dangerous for crossing over at this point to the village of Ahlish. Even now the bridge is flooded and slippery, and I guide my donkey across very carefully. We are lucky to have the Ourika River, because the arid land on both banks of it can be irrigated with its water and made fertile for growing palm trees and fruit trees and vegetables and grass.

Not everywhere in our country do big rivers flow. Many regions have to depend on rain alone for water — and Allah knows there is no relying on it. Sometimes no rain falls there at all throughout a whole year! Then the fields get burned by the scorching sun and there is

almost no harvest and everybody has to borrow *dirhams* for wheat and flour and oil and sugar and mint tea.

Some people are already on their way back from the *souk*. They came before sunrise, and have to walk for many hours before they reach their villages again.

Others go first to the *caïd*'s house. The *caïd* is the judge who comes here on every *souk* day to hold court. When people have a quarrel or an argument over a piece of land, they always go to the *caïd* for help. Even family troubles and disputes about inheritances are decided by the *caïd* in the weekly Court of the Law. People sit for hours in the courtyard and wait till the *caïd* calls them in to have their cases heard and judged. Sometimes there are arguments in the *souk*, too, or even a theft occurs, and then the culprits are brought at once before the *caïd*. If they are caught, that is.

III

Hundreds and hundreds of donkeys are already standing on the shore of the Ourika River, where their owners leave them to graze on whatever thistles they can find on the stony ground. Mohammed and I lead our animals to the pottery square and unload our wares, before we take them to the grazing place too.

"You chose the right spot!" I call to Ahmed ben Je'aar, the *tagia* knitter. "I wish I had such a tree to hang my *gidrahs* on for everybody to see!"

Ahmed and his brother Ali not only sell their *tagias* under the tree; they knit them here too, all day long. Only men knit *tagias*, anyway.

"Allah be praised for the tree," Ahmed answers. "It gives us shade. Don't you want new *tagias* for your father and yourself to wear tomorrow? You surely will go to the Independence Day celebrations, and you wouldn't go without a fine, colorful new *tagia*, would you?"

"*You* will sell well today, I am sure," I answer. "But will I? There are so many potters in the *souk* already. If I sell well, I will buy a *tagia* for my grandfather from you. Please keep one of the two blue ones with no design for me. I will come back for it later."

"*Insh'allah,*" he replies. "May you sell every one of your *gidrahs!*"

At the donkey yard, we tether our animals to the ground by tying the end of the long chain to a heavy stone, so they can't wander away.

Mohammed and I spread our wares out opposite each other so that the strollers have to pass between us, and then we begin to call for customers.

"*Gidrahs! Gidrahs!*" I shout. "Beautiful *gidrahs!* Your *kouskous* will taste like honey if you cook it in my pots! Buy them! Try them!"

"*Gidrahs!* The best *gidrahs!*" my friend Mohammed wails in a loud voice. "I need a few *dirhams*, quick, because I have hurt my foot and must go to the medicine seller. Have pity! Help me! I am selling cheap, good people!"

People stop and laugh, and a man buys one of my friend's *gidrahs*.

"Mohammed's *gidrahs* are the best!" I shout out loud for everybody to hear.

"No!" shouts my friend. "Mohammed's *gidrahs* are the best!"

"Don't believe him," I call again. "Mohammed's *gidrahs* are the best!"

People stop and listen.

"Are you both plagued by *jinn?*" asks an old man. "Who is this Mohammed, anyway, whom you both praise so much?"

"I am Mohammed!" I announce.

"I am Mohammed!" my friend echoes me. The onlookers start laughing, and soon we both have a crowd around us, and sell quite a few *gidrahs*, especially since our prices are low.

"Your onion soup will taste like honey in my *gidrahs!*" I shout.

"Did you say that onion soup will taste like honey if I cook it in one of your pots?" asks a boy in a booth a few steps away.

"Yes, I did," I answer. "Try one yourself."

"That's what *you* think," he says. "I am Abdullah the beehive maker and I know what honey tastes like. If people want to taste honey, they have to buy my beehives and not your miserable pots. Honey is like the praise of Allah, and you talk nonsense."

"What in the name of Allah do you want from the boy?" Ali the barber interrupts. "He wants to sell; let him sell! Did he offend your beehives? Why do you make such a sour face? Come over and I will make it smile again with a bit of soap. I have heard you praise your beehives often enough and you always say they will keep as long as the best carpets of sheep's wool. Does that offend the sheep? Be peaceful, and mind your own wares, Abdullah!"

I am glad for what Ali has said to Abdullah, and we go on praising our wares and selling quite well.

28

"Mohammed," I say, "I have an idea. I see Chussa the blacksmith over there. Keep an eye on my *gidrahs*. I will be back soon."

"I will sell first one of my own *gidrahs* and then one of yours. Afterwards, you can do the same for me while I go for a walk! But don't bring Chussa here to look after my foot," he warns me, "or I will make trouble for you. I am going to Kadur the medicine seller later. He will give me some ointment for it."

"Don't be silly, Mohammed. Chussa has better things to do than to fuss with your foot!"

"Mohammed's *gidrahs* are the best!" he calls out again as I walk away. "Buy Mohammed's *gidrahs,* good people!"

"*Saba el cheh,* Chussa ben Hamid," I greet the blacksmith. "May Allah send you many buyers!"

"*Saba el cheh,* Mohammed," he answers. "How does Allah treat your father's life? Is he well? I haven't seen his face for a long time — for three or four *souk* days, I think."

"Abba can't come to the *souk*. If he didn't work every day, there wouldn't be enough *dirhams* in the house to buy food. And we have to save for the tax collector too, he says."

"Allah is in heaven, but the tax collector walks on earth." Chussa chuckles. "I know, I know. And he walks around the market too. May Allah make your father satisfied — he is a good man. And what is on your mind, Mohammed?"

"I want to ask you a favor, Chussa ben Hamid. Can you lend me ten donkey shoes? I would need them only till the *muezzin* calls to midday prayer."

"What do you need the shoes for?"

"I want to string them up above my *gidrahs,* so they will catch the eyes of the people."

"By the beard of the Prophet, as true as I am Chussa the blacksmith, I have never heard of displaying iron shoes with *gidrahs* so they might sell better! Who gave you that wisdom? Or is it foolishness? Young people can think up more strange things nowadays than old men can understand. Well, people once thought Hassan the Fool was stupid, and they paid for it with a house. Who am I to judge? Here, take the ten donkey shoes, and may Allah help you with your crazy idea."

I know my friend Mohammed is selling for me too, so I don't have to hurry, and I ask Chussa to tell me about Hassan the Fool.

"Chussa is telling a story!" I call out, and quickly a small crowd gathers before the blacksmith, who is known for his storytelling. He loves nothing better.

"Hassan the Fool," begins Chussa, "lived long ago in the beautiful city of Marrakesh. His parents had left him a fine stone house with a wide courtyard beautified with fountains and sweet-smelling flowers. It was cool in summer and warm in winter in his house. But his neighbor Mustafa envied him the house and became his enemy.

"One day, Hassan had fallen asleep while guarding the Sultan's treasures, and a thief stole a precious gold dagger studded with jewels. Hassan was sentenced to fourteen days in prison, to fourteen lashes with the whip, and to a fine of twenty-five pounds of silver.

"The fourteen days in prison didn't bother Hassan, because he loved company, and he had many friends in the prison anyway. The fourteen lashes with the whip he didn't mind too much either, because he had bribed the prison warden with fourteen *dirhams,* and the warden had sold him a pair of underpants which were stuffed with straw and pieces of leather to soften the strokes. But where could he find twenty-five pounds of silver?

"It was then that his neighbor Mustafa visited him in prison. He had brought mutton and *kouskous* for him to eat, and he pitied him no end.

31

" 'I cannot see you suffer,' he said. 'I know you will have to stay in prison all your life if you don't pay the fine, and so I have come to help you!'

" 'Like a bad *jinni* you will,' thought Hassan, but aloud he said: 'May Allah help you the way you help me, O my selfless friend!'

" 'I have sold all the jewelry of my two wives,' wailed Mustafa, 'and I am willing to buy your house, so you can pay the fine and be free again.'

" 'My house is worth a hundred pounds of silver,' said Hassan, 'and I need only twenty-five pounds. What shall I do with the rest and no house?'

" 'You need not worry, O friend of my heart. I have even thought of that! In order that you will not have to worry about what to do with all the money, I will give you only twenty-five pounds of silver. This way, you will be free from prison *and* free from worry!'

" 'And without a house either!' said Hassan. 'The plague on you and your house, not including your honorable wives!' But he had no choice, if he didn't want to stay in jail forever. So he sold his house to Mustafa, and had the scribe and a lawyer called in to set up the contract.

" 'My heart bleeds, when I think of my fine house,' Hassan the Fool said to Mustafa. 'I will sell you the house for twenty-five pounds of silver, but allow me one clause in the contract. I want to have the right to come into one room in the house whenever I want to.'

" 'Rightly are you called a fool,' thought Mustafa, and he agreed gladly.

" 'In this room I want to own one single thing,' Hassan continued.

" 'And this is?'

" 'A strong nail in the wall and the right to hang on it my coat or anything else I want to.'

" 'Fool indeed!' thought the lawyer, and as Mustafa agreed again, he set this clause down in the contract. Mustafa embraced Hassan with tears in his eyes and congratulated him on his freedom. He even gave him one pound of silver so he could rent a little hut to live in.

"Hassan was free now, and lived in his hut. Mustafa had his new house repaired and painted and richly decorated. He put the finest tiles on the walls of the house. After this was all done, he moved in with his family.

"On this very day, Hassan the Fool went to the slaughterhouse. He bought the hind leg of a donkey and carried it to his former house. There he went straight to the finest room, drove a big nail into the wall, and hung the leg of the donkey on it.

"Mustafa was horrified. 'The meat will start smelling before the *muezzin* calls for the evening prayer!' he cried.

" 'I hope so,' said Hassan the Fool, 'but I have the right to hang on my nail whatever I like! May Allah give your noses a pleasant time!' and with that he left the house. The next day, Mustafa came to him and implored him to take the donkey leg away. 'My wives are very sensitive about smells,' he said. 'Here are two silver pounds. I will buy the nail from you for this princely sum.'

" 'My heart is attached to it,' answered Hassan. 'It is not for sale.' And he went to the house to make sure the donkey leg was still hanging there.

"The days went by. The whole house stank of rotting meat and thousands of flies scurried all over the place. Mustafa went to the *caïd* to complain, but Hassan showed the contract and insisted on his right. After eight days, Mustafa said to Hassan, 'You win! Give me my twenty-five pounds of silver and the eight pounds of silver I spent for the repairs and decorations, and you can have your cursed house back, you fool!'

" 'Twenty-five pounds of silver for such a stinking house!' cried Hassan. 'Never! I know you are a poor miser, so here are five pounds of silver for the house, take it or leave it.'

"They went to the lawyer and had a new contract drawn up. Mustafa sold the house back to Hassan for five pounds of silver. 'Including the donkey leg?' Hassan asked. 'Or would you rather take it with you? I don't need it any more!' "

We all laugh and praise Chussa the blacksmith for the good story. Ah, if I could tell stories like that, I would become a storyteller!

I run back to my friend and string the ten donkey shoes up above our *gidrahs*, while I tell Mohammed the story of Hassan the Fool.

"I sold two of your *gidrahs* while you were away," Mohammed reports proudly.

"That makes seven already! By Allah! I forgot to eat my dates!" I take them out, give Mohammed two, and eat five myself. "Give me the pits," I say. "I need them for counting."

"It may not be great news to you, but you are a fool too," Mohammed laughs, and he spits the pits in my hand. "If you want *more* pits, there are many more on the ground here." But then I explain to him my reason for collecting date pits.

"My foot hurts even more now when I stand up," says Mohammed. "I want to go to the medicine seller. Now it's your turn to sell for both of us." And he hobbles off.

Soon a crowd collects in front of my wares. Some shake their heads and ask what this nonsense of displaying donkey shoes means, and others laugh or tease me, but while they stand there and talk, they look at the *gidrahs* too, and I praise them, and explain that they are all bargains. Truly, it doesn't take long till only four of my *gidrahs*

are left, and six of Mohammed's. For each of my own *gidrahs* sold, I eat a date, but that only makes me feel more hungry. I go over quickly to the date sellers and buy half a kilo of dried Erfoud dates. The date harvest last winter was very good, may Allah give us always plenty of them.

After a long while, my friend Mohammed comes back, with a piece of cloth around his foot.

"There was a splinter in the toe," he says, "and it hurt when Kadur took it out. He smeared some ointment on it and said it will be all right again tomorrow, but he also said that I'd better not walk around on it today. If you want to, you can roam around the *souk*. I have to stay here anyway, with my sore foot."

"Thank you, Mohammed! You know, you are lucky Kadur took the splinter out. You will have to walk quite a few hours to the big *fantasia* tomorrow, and you need healthy feet for that. You don't want to limp all the way. And the donkey shoes will bring us luck, *insh'allah!* I hope we will sell all our *gidrahs!*"

It has been a wonderful selling day so far, and I can hear the *dirhams* jingling in my *shkara* as I start out again to stroll through the *souk*.

IV

I walk through the grains and the vegetable markets and on to the street of the grocery stalls. I pass the soap stands and the pancake bakers, and stop at the pastryman's to buy a *grioush*. It looks like a coiled snake, but is a sweet-tasting pastry fried in oil. I love it.

I stroll through the street of prayer rugs, pass the copper stalls and the basket shops, and walk down the street of dates till I come to the spice bazaar.

In the next alley, the stands are full of incense and olive oil and sugar cones. Then come the cloth merchants, and soon I am in the little square of the medicine and henna shops.

There sits Kadur ben Mohammed with baskets full of herbs and medicines.

"*Saba el cheh!*" I greet him. "My grandfather sends you his greetings and wants you to know that his back aches more than ever."

"*Ma'al salama!*" he answers. "Peace be with you, grandson of my old friend Yussuf. I will give you a few ounces of my *sahtar* herb. Tell him to boil the leaves and rub the juice in, and he will feel like join-

ing the dancers tomorrow at the Independence Day festival. It is only twenty *francs*, because he is my old friend."

"Jiddy wants you to know that he has already rubbed many *dirhams* worth of your *sahtar* herb into his back, and it has helped him as much as if he had eaten the *dirhams* instead."

"He must have rubbed in the *sahtar* the wrong way," Kadur laughs. "I will give you a wild desert onion for him this time, but tell him to eat it raw and not to rub it in. And he probably forgot to put the panther fur I sold him on his aching shoulders at night. The cold night air is poison for his old bones."

Kadur takes a big desert onion from a basket, and I pay him thirty *francs* for it. In the other baskets, he has many more herbs and ointments and medicines; *dru*, the tree bark one makes incense from; henna leaves; *imsachen*, a plant which is good for all ailments of the heart and the liver; the wild *eljeg* fruit, which the women boil to extract blue juice for beauty marks on their faces and hands; and many others.

In the open shop behind him, his son sells medicines too. The women crowd around there and choose from the herbs and ointments and powders, and skins and teeth of snakes and wild animals.

37

Over the entrance hang dried mice, cats' tails, and foxes' teeth, the heads and skins of wild boars, antelopes, gazelles, jaguars, panthers, and leopards. Many medicines are made from the entrails of these wild animals. The skins are especially good for rheumatism and gout, says Kadur. He sells amber necklaces too, which the women wear as adornments.

"What ails you, my friend?" Kadur calls to a boy who is looking at him with a pained expression.

"My stomach hurts," he answers. "I ate a can of old sardines, and my stomach doesn't like it, and my mother wants me to buy a cup of castor oil and drink it here, but I won't. I hate castor oil! I'd rather have a stomach-ache."

"Castor oil is old-fashioned anyway," Kadur consoles him. "*Ashi hena!* I have something better for you! I will brew you some *sahtar.*

38

That will make your stomach trouble disappear as if a good *jinni* had taken it away." With that, he warms water over a small kerosene stove in the shop.

"Didn't you say that *sahtar* helps against backache?" I ask, surprised.

"Against backache, if you rub it in. Against stomach-ache, if you drink it. Against dandruff, if you distill it, and against bad teeth, if you chew it."

"What does it taste like?" asks the boy suspiciously.

"Like honey with sesame seed!" Kadur assures him. "Try it once and you will love to have stomach-ache just for the pleasure of drinking my *sahtar* brew." He hands him a cup of it. The boy tastes the brew cautiously, but then his face brightens.

"You put mint leaves and sugar in it too, I am sure," he

says. "Thank you! How much do I have to pay?"

"Ten *francs*," says Kadur, "because you are my friend — like everybody. Here, take a few more *sahtar* herbs. Have your mother brew you a cup of it tonight, and one tomorrow morning, and you will feel like a grasshopper in a wheatfield."

I buy half a *dirham's* worth of henna leaves for my mother, put them in my *shkara* with the wild desert onion, and walk on through the crowded alleys of the *souk*.

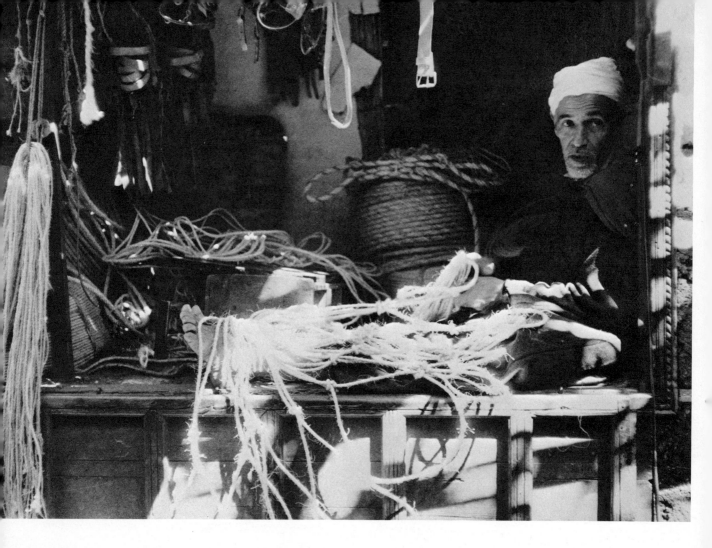

Hassan the ropemaker sits in his stall and works with his hands on a *gidrah* net, while he holds the ends with his toes.

"Is my father's new net finished?" I ask. Hassan nods, but then he motions me to look up to the little white village mosque. From the roof the *muezzin* begins his call to prayer.

"*Allahu akbar!*" he calls. "God is most great! *Allahu akbar! Allahu akbar!* I testify that there is no God but Allah and Mohammed is His Prophet! Come to prayer! Come to security! Allah is most great!"

The *muezzin* repeats his call four times, each time in another direction.

40

I turn my face in the direction of the Holy City of Mecca and re-cite silently the first *surah* of the Holy Koran.

"The new net is ready, son of Ibrahim," says Hassan, when he has finished saying his prayer. "I used the best halfa grass I could get. May you sell all the pottery it will hold." The halfa grass grows in the sand, and the best sandals and strongest ropes are made from it.

"Here are four *dirhams*. Abba says he will pay the rest on the next *souk* day."

"*Bismil'lah*," he answers. "In the name of Allah!" He gives me the new rope net, which I sling over my shoulders. "Bring me two small jars next time, Mohammed. One of my oil jars got broken. A customer sat on it. Did you ever hear of such a stupid man? By the beard of the Prophet, the saying is true indeed: 'Everything can be healed except stupidity.'"

In a corner next to Hassan, Rashid the scribe sits and waits for customers. When he isn't writing, he meditates.

Many men and most women in the country have never learned to read and write. When they need a letter to be written to a relative or to a business friend or a government office, or when they receive a letter, they go to a scribe with it.

Rashid doesn't only write letters. They say he writes very good charms against the evil eye and against sickness. Those against accidents or against being hit by a bullet and against *jinn*, he writes on a piece of lead. They are very expensive! The words of the charms are taken from the Koran, but he includes also the name of the one who is to wear it, and that of his mother.

I would like to become a scribe myself one day, but it would take years before I could write well enough and recite many pages of the Koran by heart.

"Can you write a charm that would make me rich?" I whisper to Rashid.

"Real riches do not come from an abundance of goods, my boy," Rashid answers with his eyes closed, "but from a contented mind. That only *you* can bring about, and the will of Allah, may He protect you. No charm can make you rich."

A slap in the back makes me turn abruptly.

"*Ma'al salama!*" calls my brother Ahmed, and grins at me. "*Kif inta?* How are you? Your friend Mohammed told me you sold well! *Dirhams, dirhams, dirhams,* where are they?"

"Number one," I say, "as you ask me how I am, I will answer: I am well enough to give you a slap that will put you to sleep for an hour at least. Number two: what in the name of our Prophet made you weasel out of the Koran school and come here, where you have no business to be? Number three: stop grinning like an innocent idiot, I *know* you are only trying to fool me. Answer, and quick, or else!" And I shake him by the shoulders.

"It was your friend Mohammed who told me to come here, when I was looking for you in the *souk*," he wails.

"You know very well what I mean, you monkey. Who allowed you to play hooky today?"

"If you let go of me, I'll tell you," he answers. "And I didn't come to you for a beating, you big mule, you! I came for help and that's what I get from my own brother! I came because I wanted you to help me and my friend Omar with our goat."

"What goat?" I ask severely, while I walk on to buy a sugar cone.

"A few weeks ago, Omar and I found a kid in the desert, and no owner could be found, and it was almost dead, and we fed it till it was well again. You know all about it, anyway."

"Well, I forgot. I have other things to think of. Go on, Ahmed!"

"Omar and I wanted to sell the kid today, and we drove it here, but it was such hard work! Omar is still on his way. I ran on to tell you. Please help him sell it. I have to be back so I won't miss afternoon school, at least. I hope I get a ride back on a mule — "

"Hide! Quick!" I whisper to Ahmed. "Here comes Jima, of all people!"

But it is too late. Jima stops right in front of us, and all Ahmed can do is cover his face with his fists.

Jima has brought little Hamidu along on her back. She stops the mule in front of us and calls down in surprise:

"I sent *one* son to the *souk*, and now I see *two*. Ahmed, take your silly hands away from your face, you naughty boy. Do you think I

44

don't see *you* because you don't see *me*? Wait till you come home! Why are you not in school?"

People have stopped and are laughing at Ahmed, who is so ashamed he keeps on holding his fists before his eyes.

"It was really very important for Ahmed to come," I defend him, and tell our mother the whole story; but of course I make it a bit more important, so she won't get angry.

"Give me a few *dirhams*," Jima says to me. "I had to ride here to buy dyes for my wool. I might as well take the sugar cone along myself and the dates too. You can go back, Mohammed, and finish selling our *gidrahs*. As for you, Ahmed, if you are not back at your Koran school by the time it starts again, I myself will spank you! I don't care how you get back — but you'd better be quick!"

With that, Jima dismounts and starts bargaining with the dye merchant. My brother and I make haste to get away, before she can start asking us more questions.

"The sheep and goat market is long over. You should have known better than to drag the kid here this late. Run along to your friend and bring the kid close to the road. Offer it to the people on their way home, and tell them it is a big bargain, because you have missed the market. *Yallah!* Disappear! Quick!" And I give him a slap for good measure, before he runs off.

On the way back to my *gidrahs*, I stop at a mint-tea stall. I am not sure which leaves to choose. The man is not very friendly. "Don't squeeze the leaves, or they will smell of your dirty hands instead of mint," he grumbles. "The peppermint tea withers in the hands of those who do not know how to handle it! *Yallah!* Look for somebody else who will empty his basket for you, so that you can choose the best leaves! Not me! *Yallah! Yallah ruah!*"

"My hands are not dirty," I answer, and another man comes to my aid. "Don't darken the beautiful day with your bleak voice," he says. "Why don't you teach the boy how to choose the right leaves instead of scolding him?" He helps me pick out four nice bundles for forty *francs*. I pay and put them in the hood of my *djellaba*.

"In the name of Allah, where were you and why did you stay so long?" Mohammed asks me, when I come back to the *gidrahs*. "Your silly brother was here, and then your mother passed by too, and everybody wanted to know where you had gone. Here are four *dirhams.* I sold your last four jars, and I have only two of mine left. You needn't wait for me."

I give Mohammed four more of my dates. He gives me the pits, and I take my *gidrah* net. Then I take the iron shoes back to Chussa ben Hamid. I thank him and ask his forgiveness for being late.

"Did they bring you luck?" he asks, and when I say they did, he gives me one as a present to take home.

I fasten the two nets on the back of my donkey. Then I bring him water from the Ourika River and a bit of grass which I buy from a vendor for ten *francs,* and ride home. I am glad I don't have to walk this time.

On the way out I stop at the *tagia* tree and buy the blue cap I had chosen this morning for Jiddy.

People and donkeys carry clay pots and *gidrahs* and bundles of wheat and grass they have bought at the *souk,* and bags with flour and dates, and goats and sheep, and cloth for *djellabas,* and sugar

cones and meat and eggs and other foodstuffs. Everybody has bought or traded something. It was a good *souk* today.

I pass the bridge again and look out for Ahmed and his friend with the kid. But it's quite a while before I see them. When I do, I stop and watch. Omar stands close to the road with his arms around the kid's neck. My brother Ahmed stops people and offers them the kid. Omar then holds it up in his arms and looks pleadingly at the prospective buyers.

Nobody wants the kid, and Ahmed begins to wail at the next man:

"Have pity on my poor friend! He has no father, no mother, only uncles and aunts, and tomorrow there will be no food in the house if he doesn't sell the kid! Have pity, gracious, generous friend, buy his kid! Allah will bless you for it!"

At last a man on a donkey stops. There are sheep in his saddle pouches, and he holds two little lambs in his arms. He looks at Omar suspiciously.

"Where did you get the kid?" he asks sternly. I ride up to him and say:

"I know this boy. He is from our village, Tafsa. I can testify that the kid belongs to him. I speak the truth, as Allah is great!"

"And how much does he want for that miserable, skinny creature?" the man asks Ahmed.

"Only fourteen *dirhams*," he answers, "because the boy must bring money home, or else he will be — "

The man starts laughing. "You know all the tricks of a donkey dealer," he says. "Here are six *dirhams*; that's good money for the kid."

"My friend will be beaten if he brings home only half of what the kid is worth," Ahmed says with a sad face, and I can barely keep from grinning. What a nerve my brother has!

"Take eight *dirhams*, then, and tell the uncles and aunts that your friend got one *dirham* more than the kid is worth. *Yallah*, now, I can't stay here forever." He gives Ahmed eight *dirhams* and Omar

brings him the kid. I help the man put one of the little lambs into the hood on his back, and he takes the kid in front with the other lamb, before he rides on.

"May Allah lengthen your days!" Ahmed and Omar shout after him.

"That was a good deal!" Ahmed says. They divide the money and mount my donkey. One sits in front of me, one in back.

I give Ahmed and Omar some of the olives and the *chubz* I still have in my *shkara*, and we munch them while we ride along. We pass many people who are going home from the *souk*, mostly men and boys. Women and girls rarely go to the market to sell. They gather brushwood on the hills for the fire, or carry water jars from the wells, or cut bits of grass wherever they can find it along the paths through the fields.

Not far from our village, three girls wave to us from a hill and then come running down with big bundles of brushwood on their backs. One of them is my sister Latifa.

"Mohammed!" she shouts. "Mohammed! Stop! *Ashi hena!* You are just in time. Get off the donkey and put our brushwood on. We are on our way home!"

"That's the end of our ride, unless we get away from here fast!"

50

says Ahmed, and I start teasing my sister: "What a strange coincidence! We are on our way home too!"

"I will put salt in your tea if you don't stop and let the donkey carry our bundles, Mohammed!"

"Salted tea will protect us from *jinn!*" cries Ahmed happily. "Put it in, put it in!" But to me he says, "I think we'd better stop teasing Latifa, or Abba will spit fire, if he hears of it."

I too think we have made the girls angry enough by now. The brushwood is for the village kiln, where the *gidrahs* and bowls and pots are being fired.

We fasten the bundles of brushwood on the donkey and walk the last part of the way together to our village. At the kiln, we unload the brushwood on top of a huge pile. Then Latifa and I go home, while Ahmed runs on to the Koran school.

"Jima has already come home!" I say in surprise to Lalla, our grandmother, when I see the sugar cone and the soap and a bagful of greens on the step to our bedroom. "She must have taken the camel path across the hills."

V

I go to look for Jima, and find her leading our cow out to the field. I give her the mint-tea leaves and the *dirhams* I earned, and tell her that I am going up to see my friend Ali.

"No, you aren't," she answers. "Take your *djellaba* off and help your father turn the new vessels in the sun."

When a new piece of pottery is finished, it has to dry evenly in the sun for two days. For this reason, every pot and *gidrah* and jar must be turned four times between sunrise and midday prayer, and four times again between midday prayer and sundown, so that every part of the clay gets the same amount of sunshine.

"Did you sell well?" Abba asks me, when I hand him the new *gidrah* net.

"Every *gidrah* you gave me!" I answer proudly. I tell him about the donkey shoes which I had hung up to attract customers, and he laughs heartily.

"I am happy you sold so well, my son," he says. "Allah knows we need every *franc*."

"People know that your pottery is especially good. Quite often they asked me whether I came from Tafsa."

"My pottery is indeed very good," Abba says with a sly smile, "but the credit for it belongs really to our Tafsa clay. I brought some up from the riverbank this morning and spread it out on the ground over there to dry. Do you see how red it is?"

"Yes, and it glimmers in the sun."

"It's the metal in it that glimmers. There are two kinds of clay. One is the white *therakht*. The pottery made from it breaks easily. But our clay is the *er-asr* sort, the honey clay. It makes a harder vessel,

because there are bits of metal in it. You can even hear it; it gives a fine metallic sound when you tap it."

"Everybody did that today, before buying," I remember now.

"Of course. The sound tells the quality, and gives the slightest crack away."

After we have turned the clay vessels, I go with Abba to his workshop and squat beside him, while he turns the potter's wheel.

Abba sits with his back against the wall and lets his legs dangle down into a pit, where his feet rest on a horizontal wheel. A beam comes up from the center of the wheel to the level of the floor, and on it sits a small disk. Abba dumps a few handfuls of wet clay on the disk and starts turning the wheel with his feet, while he squeezes

the clay between his hands. This makes the disk rotate — either fast, when he turns the wheel quickly, or slow, when he slows down.

More and more clay is added, and now Abba forms the belly of a new water jar by turning the wheel fast with his feet and pressing the clay firmly between his hands, from the inside as well as from the outside.

I never could do it that well. It takes many years of learning to form the lumps of clay into a beautiful vessel.

"I don't think I will ever be able to make such a fine *gidrah*," I say. "And I don't think I want to become a potter anyway."

Abba smiles. "Don't you like working at the potter's wheel?" he asks.

"Oh yes, I do. But you work seven days a week from sunrise to sundown, and still it brings us not enough *dirhams* to buy everything we need."

"You speak the truth, Mohammed, you speak the truth. If Jiddy didn't have his twenty date palms, we would be hungry more often than not."

"Everybody praises your work, Abba, and we never forget to praise Allah. You nailed the skull of our dog for good luck on the wall above your potter's wheel after he died last month, and we pray five times every day, and Jima and you and Jiddy and Lalla work all day long. Why do we still have to stay poor all our lives, then, and why are many people rich?"

"It is all in the hands of Allah, Mohammed. Otherwise it might be even worse. There is an old saying: 'Allah distributes the blessings — if Man did it, many people would receive nothing at all.'"

"But I have also heard that our country isn't really poor at all, Abba. There is oil in the earth, and some is already being taken out. There are iron ore and cobalt and asbestos and many minerals down in the earth. Why doesn't it make us all a bit better off?"

"Fish are not sold on the bottom of the sea, Mohammed. We have even more riches in our soil than you just said, but we have to take them out from there first!

"We could build many factories and produce many fine things, if we only knew *how* to do it. But very few people in our country know

enough yet. Most children don't even know how to write and read. I am happy you have learned how. Now I hear that soon every child will *have* to go to a government school! When they grow up, we will have enough good teachers for all those things they study in Europe and in America—and then we will build factories and hospitals, and will have engineers and architects, and then at last there will be work enough and food enough for everybody."

The shadows have grown longer, and it is too dark now for Abba to go on working, so we clean our hands and walk over to the kitchen.

"Abba, I wish I could become a teacher," I say.

"*Insh'allah!* We will talk about it, Mohammed, my son, but now let us eat."

Jima is baking fresh *chubz* on the clay oven. When it is ready, she tears it into small pieces and throws these on the big basket plate.

"It looks like *chubz*," says Abba jokingly, "and it tastes like sesame, but it smells like cedar resin and almond trees. What strange spices did you use today?"

"I used only sesame for the *chubz*," answers Jima. "but your nose is right. I bought cedar cones on the market and boiled them to get green dye, and I boiled the bark of the almond tree for red color, and apple-tree leaves for brown and pomegranate rinds for yellow dye. That's what you smell. Come and eat, all of you."

We squat around the big basket plate, say "*Bismil'lah*," eat our *chubz*, and drink water with it. Afterwards, Jima takes the big bowl with *kouskous* from the oven: this is wheat cereal, cooked with oil, water, vegetable, and spices. We dip three fingers of our right hands into the mash, roll it into small balls, and drop them into our mouths. Today, because I sold well at the *souk*, we all have sweet mint tea after the meal, and dates dipped in honey.

56

When we hear the *muezzin* announcing the setting of the sun, Abba and Ahmed and I step outside, turn our faces to the Holy City of Mecca, and pray in silence.

The fire in the clay oven near our house is kindled. The vessels get strong and hard in the heat of the kiln, where they will stay for two hours. Every evening a different potter uses the kiln. Tonight it is our turn. I walk up to Jiddy, who squats by it, and give him the wild onion I bought. I tell him the message Kadur ben Mohammed gave me and he laughs. "My *francs* surely will help fill Kadur's money purse, but I am not so sure this onion will heal my backache!"

It gets dark quickly, and no one in the village has electricity or any other artificial light. I am tired and go to our room, where my brothers and sisters are already asleep. I take my sandals off, lie down on my reed mat, and cover myself with my *djellaba*. My upper lip itches again — surely I won't meet an old friend at night? Maybe I will dream of one. *Insh'allah!* I think, and I too fall asleep quickly.

VI

"Mohammed! Latifa! Hadid-sha! Quick! Wake up!" I hear Ahmed's voice calling. I rub my eyes, jump from my mat, and ask what has happened. Ahmed is kneeling in the window hole, and his body fills the opening, so I can't see what's going on. I step outside and look, but still I can't see anything special.

"What did you wake us up for so early, you braying donkey?" I ask my brother.

"A sultan's descendant has just been flying past," he asserts.

"Has a *jinni* got hold of you that you talk such nonsense? If you are lying, I'll make you see stars dancing before your eyes and feel a rope drumming on your behind!" I threaten him. "Now, how are you going to wriggle out of it, my brother? Quick now — or else!" I grab a piece of rope, and my sisters encourage me to give it to him good this time.

"Patience, my brother!" Ahmed mocks me. "Patience, my sweet sisters, haste makes for injustice, I have learned! Do you see the stork up there?"

"Of course I do. I saw him long before you, when he settled on our house yesterday."

"This stork is a descendant of a sultan!"

"And you are the Sheik of Marrakesh!" I mock him. "My rope gets impatient!"

"Long ago, sweet brother and sisters," Ahmed continues like a storyteller, "a very arrogant sultan insulted a group of devout pil-

58

grims on their visit to a saint's shrine because they didn't make way for him at once. When one of the pilgrims warned him to be more humble in the presence of the saint's tomb, he hit him with a rope, and killed him. I think it was a rope like the one in your hand, O Mohammed!"

"Never mind my rope. Go on!" I order him.

"Allah saw it. He got very angry and at once He turned the sultan into a stork. When the sultan saw where his bad manners had got him, he cried bitterly and regretted in his heart what he had done.

"Allah said, 'I will not change you back again, but I will make you and your descendants the bearers of good omens.' Ever since, the storks seek the friendship of human beings, and they like nothing better than to build their nests on the rooftops. So I was right when I said a descendant of a sultan was flying above our house, wasn't I?"

"Did you make up that story?" I ask, as I swing my rope.

"No, the *taleb* told it to us in the Koran school."

"Go away," I answer, "but quick, before my rope forgets that you are my father's son!" Ahmed runs off making faces at me.

"Mohammed and Ahmed, go to the Sheik," Jima calls, "and tell him he can count on me for the Ourika dance today." Jima is getting ready for the festival. She takes her best dress from the cedar chest in the bedroom — the only piece of furniture we have — and Lalla helps her put it on. Then she rubs henna into the palms of her hands and stains her eyelids black.

59

Ahmed and I walk slowly up the hill to the Sheik's house. Omar the mason has just broken a hole in the wall and is inserting a wonderful latticed window. The iron latticework has been brought from Marrakesh. Omar closes the hole with a mixture of clay and straw. When the wall is dry again, he will put in the wooden shutters.

"Aren't you going to the Independence Day festival?" I ask Omar.

"Of course I'll be there," he answers. "The Sheik picked me out to ride in the *fantasia*. Watch me, I will have some tricks to show you! I will be finished with the window here long before the second prayer is called out. The Sheik expects guests after the festival, and he wants to show them his new latticed window."

Through the open door of the house, I see the Sheik drinking mint tea with our *mokallif*, our mayor.

I tell the Sheik that my mother will participate in the dance, and he asks the *mokallif* to write down her name.

Our Sheik is rich. He has beautiful red carpets spread on the floor, and two blue sofas, and even a table for his brass teapot. The *mokallif* is chosen every year by the men of the village. The Sheik is much higher in rank than a *mokallif*. He is the head of several villages, and always a rich man.

60

On the way back I see many villagers preparing for the trip to the festival. Women are washing and dressing their children and decking themselves and their daughters with heavy necklaces of amber and silver coins. The mules and donkeys are harnessed with tasseled saddles for the women. Jima hangs amulets against the evil eye around our necks and gives everybody a piece of fresh *chubz* with honey; we put a few dates and a piece of *chubz* into our *shkaras*. Jima scrubs little Hamidu clean till he screams, and ties him to her back. She packs tea leaves, sugar, a teakettle, tomatoes, sardines, and fresh *chubz* in a bag and puts it on the mule. Uncle Chussa and I help her into the saddle and she rides off. Lalla follows on her donkey. The rest of us walk. Latifa and Hadidsha go with their girl friends, Ahmed and I with Abba and Uncle Chussa.

I talk with Abba again about my plans for the future. "It takes years till you earn any money as a teacher," he says, "and I can't keep you for such a long time."

"I could earn *dirhams* on the side by embroidering *djellabas*," I say, "and I could chant *surahs* from the Koran at weddings and funerals. That would bring me enough money to study and later become a teacher."

"Insh'allah!" says Abba. "A schoolteacher never gets rich, but he rarely gets hungry either. I am paying the *taleb* every month one kilo of barley and one kilo of oil and a pound of raisins for teaching Ahmed."

"And we boys help him with the housework too," Ahmed adds.

"I don't want to become a Koran teacher," I say. "I want to become a teacher in a government school, where they teach foreign languages, how to count figures, and even drawing and chemistry and history and the like."

"Insh'allah!" says Abba again. "To learn in your youth is like engraving in stone, they say. It stays forever!"

We pass a saint's shrine on our way. Next to it, the villagers have built a Koran school and their village mosque. A group of men squats around a storyteller. We wait till enough people have assembled.

"May Allah lengthen your days, my brothers!" the man calls. "Would you like to hear how our Prophet Mohammed walked among the people? But remember first, that you all should believe in the

Koran! That all you people should be good Moslems! Generous Moslems! O people, I will tell you first the story of a swindler! Sit down and listen, listen to my story! And may Allah send to each swindler an even cleverer swindler. Listen to the story of such an unworthy one who found his master.

"A young boy was sent in times of hunger to live with his great-uncle. Now this great-uncle, may his name be forgotten, was the keeper of a shrine. He made a good living by collecting small coins and even *dirhams* from those who came to pray at the holy shrine. But although he was as fat as a greasy barrel, he was greedy and mean like a hungry desert fox.

"When the boy arrived exhausted and hungry, his great-uncle spread his hands and rolled his eyes and said, 'I wish you could stay with me, but I can barely keep myself from starving. However, as you are my brother's grandchild, I will give you my best donkey to ride on and look for work and make your fortune. Go in peace, but go!' And with this, he sent him on his way, with a piece of bread and a jar of water.

"The young boy hadn't traveled far before the donkey, which was really old and sick, and weak to boot from the little food the old miser had grudgingly given him, fell down and died.

" 'Even though the donkey is dead, I still have his carcass,' said the boy to himself. He buried it, and piled stones above the place to make it look like a saint's tomb. Soon, a pilgrim on his way to the great-uncle's shrine passed by and asked the boy what this new tomb meant.

" 'A saintly old sufferer died here,' the boy answered, 'and I buried him. Have pity and help me build him a proper shrine.'

"The pilgrim prayed at the place and left a goodly sum for the boy to build a decent shrine. Soon, more pilgrims and peasants from the neighborhood heard of the new shrine, and came to pray here too — and they all left alms. As is the case when there is a new shrine, the old one soon had fewer and fewer visitors, especially as the boy told everybody of the miraculous help he himself had found here. And this was true, my friends, because it wasn't long before the boy

64

was well off and could build for himself a fine house, even with iron grilles before the window openings.

"One day, the old great-uncle came to find out for himself what all this talk of a new tomb was about, which had almost destroyed his own good business. He was startled to find his young relative to be the keeper of the shrine and asked him to tell the truth about it. 'Who is buried in your sacred shrine?' he asked. 'I saw you come alone to my place and you went away with an old donkey.'

" 'It is the body of that miserable old donkey you gave me that lies here,' the boy answered. 'But now, you tell me the truth too: who is buried in *your* shrine?'

" 'O my boy,' answered the old man, 'we are worthy of each other. Our dear deceased are related. For in my shrine there lies the mother of your donkey!' "

We all laugh. "A plague on both of them!" says Abba, and gives the storyteller a few coins.

"It isn't proper to fool people and get rich on it!" an old man in the crowd shouts. "Allah will punish them for their dishonesty! Be honest to people and Allah will save you from evil! Be honest, people! Be honest! Teach your children honesty!"

We walk on, and soon come to a rocky stretch of desert land.

"Praise be to Allah that I meet you!" a boy calls over to us. "Where is the next well, O friends? My camels are thirsty and my tongue cleaves to my mouth. I do not know this part of the country."

He has a beautiful camel with him, and two young foals. One is black and the other is white. All three are walking in step, and it looks so funny. We greet the boy with a "*Ma'al salama!*" and tell him the way to the next well. "But first drink from my waterbag," says Uncle Chussa. "Your face and hands are covered with crusts of sand and your feet look sore. You must have come a long way."

The boy washes his mouth with a sip of water, spits it out, and then gratefully takes a few deep draughts. When I offer him my *chubz*, he breaks it in two and gives me back half. Somehow, I feel that I have seen his face before.

After eating, the boy tells us, "I have been on my way for ten days and nights. I crossed the deserts of the south. I come from Erfoud, the oasis of a hundred thousand date palms, where the great rivers Gheris and Ziz water the land."

"Erfoud, you say?" asks Uncle Chussa. "Who is your father? And where are you headed for? Haven't we met before?"

"My father is a snake charmer. When I was a child, we left here and went south. But he wants me to learn his father's trade. He sends me to his home village to live there for a while and learn to

be a potter. The village is near the Ourika River, its name is Tafsa, and —"

"And the names of your uncles are Chussa and Ibrahim!" cries my father. "And you are Jamal ben Mahmud! Praise be to Allah who made us meet our brother's son in the middle of the desert!"

We all embrace and kiss each other on both cheeks and clap each other's shoulders. Jamal can't utter a word in his surprise, and neither can I. This is like a real miracle.

"Now I know why my upper lip was itching so much yesterday," I say at last. "I *did* meet an old friend. Do you remember when we used to play together, Jamal?"

"And when we let the *taleb*'s donkey loose at night after the first day of Koran

school, because we hated going there?" he answers laughing.

"Are these your own animals?" Abba asks.

"My father gave me the camel to carry my sleeping mat and my tent, a sack with dates and some fodder and my teakettle, my *kouskous* bag and the *gidrah* and a pot for cooking. The camel with the two young foals is a present from my father to you both, for allowing me to stay with you and for teaching me how to become a good potter."

"If you had not needed the camel to carry you and your things, I would be angry with my brother," Abba says. You are welcome in my house even without a gift!"

"And if the two young foals didn't need their mother to nurse them, I too would be angry with my brother, for sending them along," Uncle Chussa adds. "You must be very tired, my brother's son; I will go back to Tafsa with you."

"I am very tired indeed," Jamal answers. "Praise be to Allah that my journey is coming to a happy end and I can rest soon. Where are the others going?"

67

"It is Independence Day today! We are going to see the *fantasia* and the big celebrations," I tell him with a wink.

"Oh, I am not really tired," he cries. "Not at all! To tell the truth, I wish you would let me come with you to the *fantasia!*"

"Tell a Berber about a *fantasia*, and he will forget food and drink and walk there even if it takes him two days and two nights," says Uncle Chussa with a chuckle. "Well then, let's go to the well and water the animals, before we continue on our way."

"Do you remember the desert song we sang so often together, when we guarded the goats?" Jamal asks me. "I had not been in a real desert *then*, but down on the other side of the High Atlas, there are more deserts than you can imagine. I sang the song often on my long walk these last ten days."

I do not remember the words, and Jamal teaches me the song again:

> *She is the desert of deserts,*
> *Has no beginning and has no end.*
> *Walk on, O my camel, walk on!*
>
> *Her sand is soft, her colors are silky,*
> *Her sand is red and is pink and is yellow,*
> *Walk on, O my camel, walk on!*
>
> *No sky is fuller of stars than the desert's,*
> *No silence is greater than her's.*
> *Walk on, O my camel, walk on!*
>
> *Nowhere is Allah nearer to us!*
> *Walk on in the garden of Allah, my camel.*
> *Walk on, O my camel, walk on!*

Soon we come to the well in the date-palm grove. We drink, water the animals, and fill our waterbags again. All of a sudden, clouds gather, the sky darkens, and gusts of sand rush toward us.

"There! There! A sandstorm again! Cover your faces!" Jamal calls excitedly. "I met so many on my way!"

"*Yallah! Yallah!*" Uncle Chussa calls to us. "Draw your hoods over your heads."

We crouch down behind the camel. Abba holds the donkey.

Now the clouds swallow the sun, and the palm trees sway forward and backward and their leaves hiss in the storm wind. But the storm is over as quickly as it came. It just went through in a big hurry.

"It looks like home here," Jamal exclaims. "You have many palm trees too."

"Oh, no," Abba answers, "not more than about two hundred, and they belong to people in our village. It's only here in this small oasis that they grow in numbers. But we are very happy with them. My father owns twenty and we will inherit them one day. We have dates from them and enough leaves for mats and baskets."

"Why don't we plant more palm trees here?" Ahmed asks.

"We can't," Uncle Chussa tells him. "Palm trees grow well only where their crowns are exposed to the blaze of the sun —"

"We have enough sun here!" Ahmed interrupts.

"Let me finish," says Uncle Chussa. "They can live only if at the same time their roots stand in water, and that means they need a lot of oasis water or river water underneath."

"That is so," Abba confirms, "and our Ourika River is very narrow and cannot spare much water."

VII

We walk on again, over stony hills and up the slopes to the southern road. It is crowded now, and we meet many neighbors and relatives from our clan. After a last bend in the road, the river valley opens suddenly to a wide plateau. This is the only big field for many miles around. It has become the festival ground for the whole Ourika Valley. Almost everybody from our Tafsa village has come today, and from Ahlish and Asni and Asul Borsh and Ahrbalou and Tafgahrt and Takhnaút, and from many other villages.

Some families have brought their tents, and thousands camp on the slopes of the hills around the festival grounds.

"They have started to parade their horses!" Uncle Chussa calls. "Let's tether our animals quickly to some trees."

We find a nice place near the road, and then I take Jamal along with me. A huge circle of men and women in their festive dresses watch the riders on their bedecked horses.

"There, Jamal, look, there come *our* riders!" and I point them out to him and tell him the name of every one. Omar is among the riders too — he really did finish the latticed window in time!

The flute players start their shrill music, and now the dancers come

70

from all sides and form themselves into groups. I see my sister Latifa with her girl friends. For once, they do not giggle and talk but wait excitedly for their turn. The music stops. The girls stand motionless and straight, till the flutes begin again with a loud wail. And now the girls start to dance slowly and solemnly, all twelve of them moving together to the right, then back, then forward and back again, always with small steps. They clap their hands, let out shrill cries, and stamp their feet. Their necklaces of silver coins jingle to the rhythm of the dance, and the flute players' taut cheeks look as if they were going to burst. The girls dance around in a half circle and make turns and sidesteps, and their skirts swirl with them. Faster and faster they dance. They have thrown their sandals off, and are dancing barefoot now. They raise their arms and yell to the music and shake their heads to all sides — till the music stops abruptly and the girls stand still like *gidrahs*. Their dance is over.

Everywhere, people are dancing and singing in groups. I have lost sight of Jamal and of my family, and wander around till I come to the group of dancers from our neighborhood. This group is made up of the best dancers from three neighboring villages. The dancers have

been selected by the Sheik to perform the Ahwash, the dance of our Ourika Valley.

The music is made by four shepherd flutes and four tambourines. One man is leading the dance, and the others follow his steps and figures.

The women dance in one row by themselves, the men in another. The men are dressed in white *djellabas,* with a silver dagger hanging at their waists. They clap their hands together and shout and move their feet and bodies from side to side and forward and backward and sideways.

There's my mother, too, dancing in the group, and she looks beautiful in her festive attire.

The music stops, and my friend Abdur steps forward with his *gambi* instrument. His father made the *gambi* from the shell of a tortoise. He plucks the goatgut strings with a flat little stick while he sings.

The clapping and the steps grow faster till the women break into shrill cries, and then suddenly the music stops and the dance has come to an end. It is burning hot here on the open field, and the dancers sweat. A man walks along the line with a big pail of water and lets every dancer have a sip.

72

"*Fantasia! Fantasia!*" I hear somebody shout. "*Fantasia! Fantasia!*"
I repeat as loud as I can, and the whole crowd takes up the cry, and
runs to the edge of the field.

Slowly, the first group of riders parades past us. They all ride
young stallions and hold their long Berber rifles upright. At the far
side of the field, they turn and ride toward us in a straight line. The
spirited horses are all in step and look eager to run.

Not far from me is the leader of the horsemen, mounted on a white
stallion. From his side hangs his silver scimitar. He watches the
line of horsemen advance. The moment they reach his level he
raises his rifle and shouts, "O Allah! O Mohammed!"

With that, the riders break into a gallop! They brandish their rifles, and the horses speed forward wildly. The horsemen let go of the reins. They raise their hands to their heads, so everybody can see they aren't holding the reins any longer. They throw their rifles into the air! They catch them in midair! They fire! The shots ring out together, and it sounds as if only one single big shot had been fired. Truly, those horsemen must be in the protection of Allah not to fall off!

The hills resound with the yells of the women, as one row of

riders after another storm in wild gallop over the field, shouting their war cries and shooting off their rifles again and again.

Clouds of dust rise into the air and the horses are foaming and stamping their feet and neighing with excitement. And now come the riders from *my* village! Omar even stands up in the saddle while he races along, and his shot comes off at the same time as the others. He is a great horseman!

The horses storm toward us — but exactly ten paces before they overrun us, they all stop. Truly, the horses are the masters of all animals! And there is no greater excitement than to see a *fantasia*.

When the *fantasia* is over, I look for my family. We sit down and eat and drink and talk, till it is time to go home again.

It is almost night when we reach our village. The moon is coming up over the hills. We sit for a long time with Jamal and talk about all that has happened today.

GLOSSARY

Abba   Father
Allahu akbar!   God is most great!
Ashi hena   Come here
Ben   Son of
Bismil'lah   In the name of Allah
Caïd   Judge
Chubz   Flat bread
Dirham   Moroccan currency, equivalent to about 20 cents. There are 100 Moroccan *francs* in one *dirham*.
Djellaba   Long cloak with a hood
Fantasia   An exhibition of horsemanship, featuring acrobatic riding and gun firing.
Gambi   Berber guitar; the body is made from a tortoise's shell.
Gidrah   Water jar, made of clay
Grioush   Sweet pastry made with honey, which looks like a coiled snake
Henna   Red dye made from a wild plant. The women use it for painting their hands and feet.
Insh'allah!   May it be Allah's will!
Jiddy   Grandfather
Jima   Mother
Jinn   Evil spirits — but there are also a few good *jinn* about. The singular of *jinn* is *jinni:*
Kif inta?   How are you?
Kilo   Kilogram, unit of measure, equal to 2.2046 pounds
Koran   The sacred book of the Mohammedans, containing the revelations to the Prophet Mohammed
Kouskous   Wheat cereal, cooked with oil, vegetables, and spices, sometimes with mutton or chicken
Lalla   Grandmother
Ma'al salama!   Peace be with you!
Mokallif   Mayor of a village
Muezzin   Caller to prayer
Na'am   Yes
Saba el cheh   Good morning
Sheik   Head of clan or tribe, also head of a few villages
Shkara   Shoulder bag of camel leather
Souk   Market
Tagia   Knitted woolen skullcap
Taleb   Teacher in a Koran school
Wadi   Dried-out river bed, river valley
Yallah! Yallah ruah!   Go! Go quick!
Zahemak   Fool

POSTSCRIPT

THE KINGDOM OF MOROCCO, with an area of 172,000 square miles, is about as big as the state of California, which it resembles in variety of scenery and climate.

Morocco fills the northwestern corner of the African continent. To the east and south, it borders on Algeria and the Sahara Desert; to the west, on the Atlantic Ocean; to the north, on the Mediterranean Sea. In Europe you can look at Morocco from the rock of Gibraltar, which belongs to England, although geographically it is a part of Spain. The town of Ceuta in Morocco is only about nine miles away from Europe. A mountain near by and the Rock of Gibraltar were called The Pillars of Hercules in ancient times. Like pillar outposts of Africa and Europe, they guard the narrow passage between the Mediterranean and the Atlantic Ocean.

Morocco has rich plains, vast deserts, and snow-capped mountains. It has modern cities like Rabat, capital and residence of the King, and Casablanca, the industrial center and port, where almost 900,000 people live in the old quarters and in the new city with its high ultramodern white buildings. But more than eighty per cent of Morocco's twelve million inhabitants live in villages all over the country, which is predominantly agricultural and pastoral.

The majority of the population are Berbers, who settled here more than five thousands years ago, during the late Stone Age. In many villages of the Atlas Mountains and its remote plains, far away from civilization, a Stone Age culture still survives.

The Arabs, who conquered Morocco in the seventh century, make up the second largest part of the population. Both Berbers and Arabs prefer to be called Moroccans. More than ninety percent of the Moroccans are Moslems, the remaining being Christians, mostly French and other foreigners, and Jews.

At the end of the seventh century the Berbers and Arabs built a powerful empire. For the seven centuries that followed, they ruled all North Africa and the greater part of Spain. At the beginning of our century, in 1912, Morocco became a protectorate of France and Spain, till at last, in 1956, the country regained its independence. Since then, many new branches of industry have been developed, and the mining of many precious minerals has been expanded. Annual phosphate production stands now at around a million tons, and there are rich deposits of copper, lead, and petroleum in the country. Cereals and dates are the main agricultural products, and Moroccan leatherwork and carpets are exported all over the world. The University of Fez is one of the outstanding centers of Islamic culture of today.

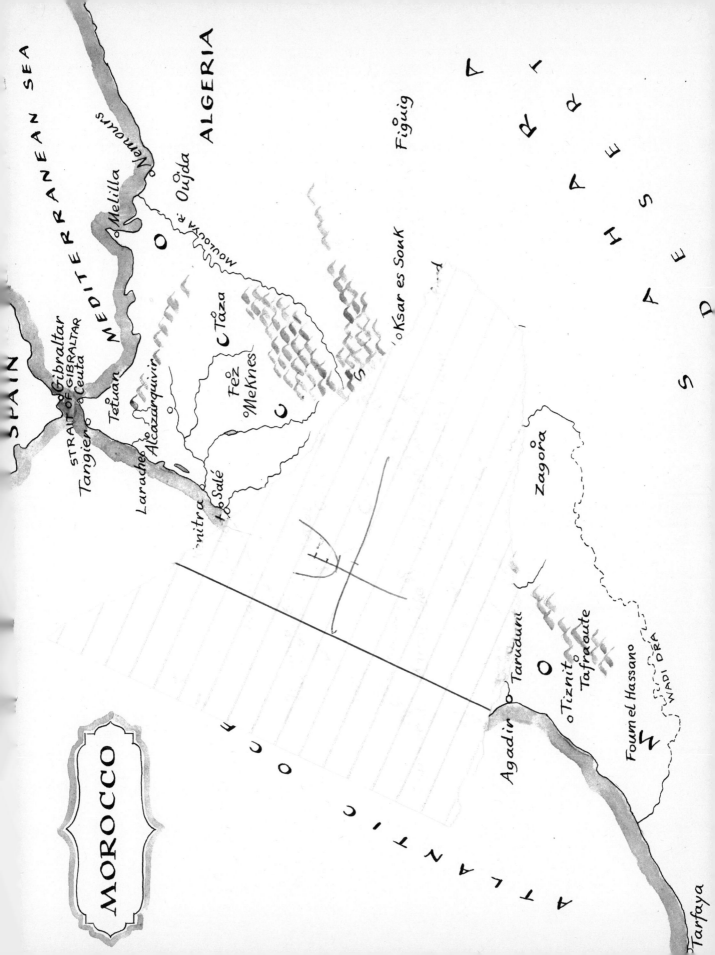

MOROCCO

SPAIN

MEDITERRANEAN SEA

ALGERIA

STRAIT OF GIBRALTAR
Gibraltar
Ceuta
Tangier
Tetuan
Melilla
Nemours
Oujda
Moulouya

Larache
Alcazarquivir
Salé
nitra
Fez
Meknes
Taza

Ksar es Souk

Figuig

ATLAS

Zagora

Agadir
Taroudant
Tiznit
Tafraoute
Foum el Hassan
WADI DRA

ATLANTIC

Tarfaya